Where is Help Needed?

Paper 13 / Paper 14 / Paper 15

	Paper 13	Paper 14	Paper 15
1	13 14 15 16 17 18 19	42 43 44 45 46 47 48 49	
2	1 2 3 4 5 6	7 8 10 12	95 96 97
3			
4	51		19 20 21
5	62 63 64 65 66	87 88 89 90 91 92	63 64 65
5A			
5B			
6		13 14 15 16 17 18 19	74 75 76 77 78 79
7	44 45 46 47 48 49	9 11	12 13 14 15 16 17 18
8	43 67		
9		20 21 22 23 24 25 26	1 2 3 4 5
10	52 53 54 55 56 57 58	1 2 3 4 5 6	58 59 60 61 62
11	7 8 9 10 11 12	27 28 29 30 31	
12	71 72 73 74 75	34 35 36 37 38 39 40 41	
13		50 51 52 53 54 55	
14	92 93 94 95 96	56 57 58 59 60 61	49 50 51 52
15	68 69 70 88 89 90 91	62 63 64 65 66 70 71	6 7 8 53 54 55 56 57
16	76 77 78 79 80 81	77 78 79 80 81 82 83 84 85 86	
17			
18	20 21 22 23 24		36 37 38 39 40 41 42
19			
19A			
20		72 73 74 75 76	
21			70 71 90 91 92 93 94
22			
23	50		89
23A			82 83 84 85 86 87 88
24	31 32 33 34 35 36 37		22 23 24 25
25			80 81
26			70 71
27			26 27 28 29
27A			
28	59 60 61 97 98 99 100	67 68 69	
28A			9 10 11
29			
30			
31			
32	38 39 40 41 42		30 31 32 33 34 35
33	82 83 84 85 86 87		43 44 45 46 47 48
34			
35			
36	25 26 27 28 29 30		
36A			
37			
38		32 33	
39		93 94 95 96 97 98 99 100	
40			

Paper 16 / Paper 17 / Paper 18

	Paper 16	Paper 17	Paper 18
1		26 27 28 29 30 31	1 2 3 4 5 6 7 8
2	14 15 16 17 18 75 76 77 78 79 80	81 82 83 84	
3	11 36 37 38 39 40		
4			
5	30 31 32 33 34 35		
5A		16 17 18 19 20	
5B			
6			9 10 11 12 13 14
7	41 42 43 44 45 46 47	76 77 78 79 80	89 90 91 92
8	12		
9		1 2 3 4	73 74 75 76
10			15 16 17 18
11	88 89 90 91 92 93	21 22 23 24 25	69 70 71 72
12		45 46 47 48 49 50	
13		39 40 41 42 43 44	
14			
15	25 26 27 28 29		19 20 21 22 62 63 64
16			
17			
18	94 95 96	9 10 11 12 13 14 15	33 34 35 36 37
19	6 7 8 9 10		
19A	65 66 67 68 69 70 71 72 73 74		
20		62 63 64 65 66 67 68 69 70 71	
21		90 91 92 93 94	53 54 55 56 57 78 93 94 95
22	19 20 21 22 23 24	51 52 53 54 55 56 57	
23		58	
23A	13		46 47 48 49 50 51 52 80
24			
25	48 49 50 51 52 53	95 96 97 85 86 87 88 89	
26	54 55 56 57 58 85 86 87	32 98 99 100	77
27			
27A		72 73 74 75	
28	81 82 83 84		23 24 25 26 27
28A			
29	97 98 99 100	59 60 61	
30			
31			
32	1 2 3 4 5 59 60 61 62 63 64	5 6 7 8	28 29 30 31 32 65 66 67 68
33			38 39 40 41 42 43 44 45 58 59 60 61
34			
35			
36			96 97 98 99 100
36A		33 34 35 36 37 38	
37			
38			79 88
39			
40			81 82 83 84 85 86 87

Paper 16

1. KM, RT	26. AISLE	51. TRACE	76. R, W
2. CLAY, RESIN	27. DAILY	52. NUDGE	77. TS, SR
3. 313, 818	28. SAILS	53. LABEL	78. DG, EH
4. PLAY, BAT	29. SLIDE	54. J	79. LS, KT
5. LABEL, VAN	30. CREAM	55. J	80. LJ, NM
6. CHEETAH, LION	31. TWO	56. M	81. 18
7. GIGANTIC, COLOSSAL	32. SON	57. A	82. 31
8. SANDAL, SLIPPER	33. NEPHEW	58. D	83. T
9. STRANGE, UNUSUAL	34. MOOR	59. WATER, KETTLE	84. 6
10. PINE, TEAK	35. WING	60. THIEF, SNEAK	85. 3
11. CARROTS	36. D	61. BUTTERCUP, SNOWDROP	86. E
12. WATER	37. E	62. SKY, CLOUD	87. I
13. 13	38. B	63. CUCUMBER, RADISH	88. POWERFUL, FEEBLE
14. LR	39. A	64. CLOCK, HAND	89. DISPERSE, GATHER
15. BC	40. C	65. 2	90. NUMEROUS, FEW
16. IB	41. 13, 17	66. 3	91. MEEK, FIERCE
17. QR	42. 3, 12	67. 6	92. REPAIR, INJURE
18. LK	43. 12, 10	68. 1	93. ELEVATE, LOWER
19. REST	44. 36, 16	69. 4	94. WINDOW
20. GOT	45. 3, 8	70. 5	95. THEATRE
21. SAFE	46. 18, 3	71. 5	96. CUCUMBER
22. STOAT	47. 4, 40	72. 3	97. NEAR
23. CURE	48. PROBE	73. 1	98. TALE
24. LEAN	49. RAID	74. 2	99. MILE
25. DIARY	50. ROSE	75. N, R	100. PAST

Paper 17

1. BEE	26. FIVE, FOUR	51. BNNM	76. 41
2. FARTHER	27. IN, CATCH	52. WUKI	77. 16
3. BUTTERFLY	28. EIGHT, ATE	53. KNUB	78. -5
4. TRICK	29. POSTMAN, DOG	54. WIKKIM	79. 43
5. THIRSTY, PARCHED	30. SISTER, AUNT	55. TREAD	80. 293
6. FIGHT, BRAWL	31. INTO, UP	56. DARE	81. RU
7. LEISURELY, SLOWLY	32. T	57. DO-A-LOT	82. IBO
8. TOO, ALSO	33. 25-9-9	58. £11.20	83. S
9. DESTROYED	34. 8x3+3 or 3x8+3	59. WISH	84. E
10. LIFELESS	35. 30÷3-3	60. HOOD	85. LEER, LATE
11. AUTOMOBILE	36. 16x4-4 or 4x16-4	61. START	86. HIVE, VANE
12. YOUTH	37. 3x6x6 (in any order)	62. 14.25	87. DEEP, FEED
13. PRAM	38. 16+4÷4 or 4+16÷4	63. 1 hr 20 mins	88. REAR, FUSE
14. JUMBLE	39. HARM, CAT	64. 8.15	89. TILE, PINE
15. FANG	40. COUNTY, USER or RUSE	65. 15 mins	90. FLEA
16. DIG	41. RAIN, STAG	66. 3	91. SPONGE
17. BEST	42. RACE, BEAT	67. 1 hr 50 mins	92. VIGOUR
18. HOOF	43. RAM, MOAT	68. 13.15	93. NUTMEG
19. SAD	44. MISER, YOUR	69. YES	94. AUNT
20. TREBLE or TRIPLE	45. ROAST	70. 10.55	95. ASTRONOMY
21. CLEAN	46. FIST	71. 250 mins	96. EXPECT
22. HOLLOW	47. PLAY	72. POLICEMAN, THIEF, BANK	97. BLEARM
23. BLOOM	48. SULK	73. WATER, BOILS, STEAM	98. B
24. REQUIRE	49. CASH	74. WHICH, PLATFORM, 4 pm	99. O
25. BRIGHT	50. OUTSIDE	75. THE, BOY, RAN	100. S

Paper 18

1. SWIFTLY, THE	26. 20	51. 25	76. HIT
2. IN, ARE	27. 14	52. 200	77. Y
3. A, BE	28. SPROUT	53. 5,2,4,1,3	78. FRIDAY
4. BROKE, FELL	29. LEMONADE	54. 5,2,4,3,1	79. 3.42 pm
5. AUTUMN, THE	30. AMSTERDAM	55. 1,5,3,4,2	80. 15 yrs
6. AIR, ANSWER	31. LAWN	56. 4,5,3,2,1	81. 5
7. MAKE, AND	32. QUEEN	57. 2,1,3,5,4	82. 6
8. FLY, CAUGHT	33. FUDGE	58. MONTH	83. 4
9. WEEK, END	34. STICK	59. JUG	84. YES
10. NOT, ICE	35. ANKLE	60. AUGUST	85. NO
11. EVERY, WHERE	36. SMELL	61. NINTH	86. 8
12. CART, ON	37. SMILE	62. 5298	87. 3
13. BE, HIND	38. GRAPE	63. 5625	88. 10.28 am
14. TAB, LET	39. PEA	64. HEAP	89. 22
15. ABLE	40. HAMLET	65. EMOTION, ANGER	90. 14
16. STOP	41. FOUR	66. SAD, NAUGHTY	91. 512
17. SCAR	42. SOLO	67. SOLE, LEATHER	92. 65
18. SKID	43. MOUSE	68. SEA, OCEAN	93. LABEL
19. 53822	44. BABY	69. DISPLEASED, CONTENTED	94. FLACK
20. 4285	45. MARBLE	70. UGLY, PRETTY	95. COAST
21. 28453	46. 18	71. SLUGGISH, ACTIVE	96. 30-15-3 or 30-3-15
22. 38425	47. 20	72. STUPID, INTELLIGENT	97. 8-5+7 or 7-5+8
23. 34	48. 40	73. SAND	98. 20÷5÷2 or 20÷2÷5
24. L	49. 20	74. FIT	99. 8x5x4 (in any order)
25. H	50. 74	75. HOLD	100. 15+5-8 or 5+15-8

Pack 3 Verbal Reasoning
Standard Version

General Advice for Parents

How should I administer the practice papers?

To get the most out of the practice papers your child should complete them in the best possible conditions - a quiet room with good lighting, and not when he Is too tired or would rather be watching a favourite television programme. Please remember that any test can be quite threatening - to adults as well as children. A practice paper was included in Pack 1 for you to work through together with your child. This practice paper introduced all the question types that your child will tackle in our verbal reasoning test papers. It may be helpful to look at this practice paper again before starting this test pack. Although Pack 3 contains a few variations of question type it mainly provides additional practice on question types that your child has already attempted. Talk through each type of question with your child to ensure that he understands what is expected of him. Ideally, you should space out the practice papers so that your child attempts no more that two papers per week. When you have marked a paper, work through it with your child, looking for ways to increase his success.

How important is timing?

Our standard practice papers are designed to take a child just under fifty minutes to complete when working at the optimum speed necessary. When your child works through one of the practice papers you should allow EXACTLY fifty minutes for its completion. This is most important since, at first, children are unaccustomed to working at the high speed which is necessary to finish all of the questions. Provide your child with a clock or watch so that he is able to pace himself. When the time is up draw a line across the page underneath the last question completed. Your child should then continue working through the test without being timed so that he can attempt all the question types contained in that particular test.

How can I help my child to finish the practice papers in the time allowed?

If your child is not completing the practice papers in the time limit, it is possible that he is spending too long puzzling over one particular type of question. It is far better to attempt twenty more questions and get them right than to spend this time struggling with a series of questions that may in the end prove too difficult. A second possibility is a lack of appropriate strategy when tackling a particular type of question. Children benefit greatly from being shown a method of approaching question types that they are finding difficult. Advice concerning the different strategies that can be adopted can be found in our publication 'Verbal Reasoning Tests Explained'. Finally, over-cautiousness may result in too much time being taken over the test papers. Some children feel the need to check and double check their answers. Such children tend to get all their answers correct but unfortunately are unable to complete the test in the time allowed. It is far better for children to complete the test and check their answers at the end if there is still time available.

Marking the test papers

The answers for the six papers in this test pack are on the following pages. Total each page of the test paper and enter the number correct in the grid provided at the front of each paper. Mark strictly and do not give your child the benefit of the doubt if the answer is difficult to read or 'almost' right.

Where is help needed?

There are thirty-eight question types in the six papers in this test pack. The chart on page four will help you to identify the question types that your child is finding difficult. For example, if your child has difficulty with questions 62-66 on Paper 13 and 87-92 on Paper 14 this would indicate that he would benefit from an explanation of Type 5 questions. Our publication 'Verbal Reasoning Tests Explained' describes each question type and gives advice on the best strategies for answering the questions.

Further advice and support

For further advice and support visit our extensive website. As well as lots of information for parents there are sample papers to download and online, timed tests for children.
The website address is

www.athey-educational.co.uk

P3S

Answers

Paper 13

1. OW, PX	26. 2×3×8 (in any order)	51. SCAMP	76. L
2. MV, LU	27. 35+37(or 37+35)-22	52. STAR	77. H
3. HX, IX	28. 5×6 (or 6×5)-4	53. THIS	78. M
4. LT, KU	29. 2×4×8 (in any order)	54. HATE	79. G
5. ER, DP	30. 9+11 (or 11+9)-5	55. TYRE	80. Y
6. PX, QX	31. OWE	56. THEN	81. S
7. SLY, CUNNING	32. TEA	57. MEAT	82. HOUR
8. UNPLEASANT, DISAGREEABLE	33. AND	58. BLED	83. SENTENCE
9. FREE, RELEASE	34. LID	59. M	84. TUG
10. HYGIENIC, SANITARY	35. WIN	60. N	85. PIGEON
11. FEEBLE, WEAK	36. AND	61. P	86. TRIO
12. INCISION, CUT	37. ATE	62. NOTE, WORD	87. COUNTY
13. RAINING, SOAKED	38. LACE	63. ROAR, SQUEAK	88. 4
14. SHEDS, GROWS	39. 12	64. CAT, EAGLE	89. 6
15. ALL, SHE	40. CELLO	65. GUN, BOW	90. 6274
16. MONDAY, DAY	41. BEEF	66. BANANA, STRAWBERRY	91. MALE
17. UNTIDY, THE (second)	42. 33	67. (d)	92. ROT
18. HER, STOOD	43. CACTUS	68. 62338	93. DOT
19. HUNDRED, THOUSAND	44. 48, 96	69. 38862	94. CAR
20. RIGHT	45. 17, 20	70. 682365	95. BAR
21. SHADE	46. 19, 25	71. PAT	96. TAKE
22. LUMP	47. 37, 50	72. BAN	97. 5
23. TRAP	48. 14, 12	73. BIT	98. 12
24. DESSERTS	49. 53, 71	74. MAST	99. N
25. 19-12+8	50. 9 pm	75. DINE	100. I

Paper 14

1. VEST	26. CALL	51. PATH, CRASH	76. CAROL
2. BALL	27. WALK, STROLL	52. ROW, GROUND	77. E
3. HARM	28. ENJOY, LIKE	53. WARD, AWAY	78. D
4. THAN	29. FIRE, BLAZE	54. QUIT, MEET	79. L
5. FAIR	30. EVERYONE, EVERYBODY	55. SPIT, PLAY	80. O
6. SING	31. MEET, ASSEMBLE	56. GOLF	81. G
7. X, C	32. 9.30 am	57. SUP	82. K
8. Q, S	33. 60 mins	58. PEAL	83. H
9. 34, 43	34. POST	59. POST	84. S
10. X, I	35. DUMMY	60. LASH	85. R
11. 20, 14	36. CORD	61. FIVE	86. W
12. V, G	37. NOON	62. 12499	87. THIN, SMALL
13. PUFF, IN	38. MESH	63. 946690	88. CONSTRUCT, DEMOLISH
14. RAIL, WAY	39. SHOW	64. 16370	89. SIX, FOUR
15. BAR, ROW	40. BUT	65. 1246690	90. SUN, GRASS
16. SOME, HOW	41. SAD	66. 7337	91. FRONT, TOP
17. KNOW, LEDGE	42. BED, JOHN	67. 12	92. PIG, COW
18. DAM, AGE	43. OUT, IN	68. 12	93. 170 m
19. BUTTER, CUP	44. MOON, COWS	69. 16	94. BETTY
20. BDFH	45. IT, IS	70. ALONE	95. 1 mins
21. HAT	46. BY, BUY	71. SILK	96. 1600 m
22. FOOL	47. THE, THOSE	72. 2	97. 210 m
23. BEAD	48. FINE, THE	73. TANYA	98. 410 m
24. TEN	49. BAG, BOOKS	74. 3	99. 450 m
25. ZOO	50. FED, BOUND	75. 0 (or NONE or ZERO)	100. ANDY

Paper 15

1. HOLD	26. SYMPHONY	51. JETTY	76. A, VOID
2. BARN	27. RESIDUE	52. FIND	77. PITCH, FORK
3. MOST	28. PRESCRIPTION	53. FOOT	78. A, WAY
4. BIG	29. INTERPRET	54. FILL	79. TRAP, DOOR
5. NINE	30. BEEF	55. FISH	80. THORN
6. 40783	31. 7	56. FIND	81. WRONG
7. 50334	32. SLEEP	57. FOAM	82. 20
8. 21-29-134925	33. BUTTERFLY	58. SHIP	83. 9
9. PIT	34. PAPER	59. STUN	84. 20
10. COT	35. METAL	60. WIND	85. 8
11. TOP	36. YELLOW	61. TRIP	86. 36
12. 5, 8	37. BATTLE	62. WASP	87. 29
13. 3, 1.5	38. STRAWBERRY	63. SHOE, FOOT	88. 120
14. 30, 0	39. CLOCK	64. BRUSH, PRINT	89. 5 km
15. 4, 9	40. BICYCLE	65. COST, CRY	90. 3, 2, 1, 5, 4
16. 2.6, 3.4	41. ENGLAND	66. TEN, HUNDRED	91. 4, 2, 3, 5, 1
17. 11, 13	42. SEVEN	67. BOSS, NOBLEMAN	92. 5, 4, 3, 2, 1
18. 5, 0	43. FEBRUARY	68. MISSED, BUSSED	93. 5, 1, 2, 4, 3
19. SYCAMORE	44. SYLLABLE	69. GRASS, MEAT	94. 3, 2, 4, 5, 1
20. CAKE B	45. NOSE	70. N	95. J
21. PAUL	46. GRAPE	71. G	96. J
22. PEA	47. WEDNESDAY	72. OVERCAME	97. Y
23. RAN	48. PURSE	73. OVERHEAR	98. P
24. PAN	49. LIT	74. PLAY, GROUND	99. V
25. RAT	50. WAR	75. SPACE, SHIP	100. O

Secondary Selection Portfolio

VERBAL REASONING
PAPER 13

FILL IN THE FOLLOWING INFORMATION BEFORE YOU BEGIN -

Today's Date_____

Your Surname (in capitals)_____

Your First Name(s)_____

Your Date of Birth_____

Read the following instructions carefully.

1. Start working at the beginning of the test and work straight through.
2. Answer the questions as quickly and as accurately as you can.
3. If you find you cannot answer any particular question do not spend too much time on it but move to the next one. Remember, if you finish all the questions on time you can return to any you have left out.
4. If you need to do any rough working you can use the side of the page if you wish.
5. If you need to change any of your answers do so clearly.
6. You will have 50 minutes to complete the test and you will be told the time after 20 minutes and 40 minutes.
7. Once you begin you will not be allowed to ask any questions.

TO BE COMPLETED BY THE PARENT -

PAGE	1	2	3	4	5	6	7	TOTAL
POSSIBLE	19	18	14	15	9	16	9	100
ACTUAL								

Athey Educational

In the following questions there are pairs of letters with a different rule governing each line. Work out the rule and complete the sequence.

A B C D E F G H I J K L M N O P Q R S T U V W X Y Z

1. KS , LT , MU , NV , (_ _ _ _) , (_ _ _ _) .

2. QZ , PY , OX , NW , (_ _ _ _) , (_ _ _ _) .

3. DV , EV , FW , GW , (_ _ _ _) , (_ _ _ _) .

4. PP , OQ , NR , MS , (_ _ _ _) , (_ _ _ _) .

5. IZ , HX , GV , FT , (_ _ _ _) , (_ _ _ _) .

6. NU , NV , OV , OW , PW , (_ _ _ _) , (_ _ _ _) .

In each of these questions underline TWO words, one from each group, which have the SAME or almost the same meaning. Here is an example.

    <u>huge</u> , elephant , cage.   giraffe , <u>massive</u> , barn.

7. simple , sly , angular.   hard , jagged , cunning.

8. happy , texture , unpleasant.   sneezy , disagreeable , old.

9. free , dirty , labour.   clean , four , release.

10. doctor , bleach , hygienic.   sanitary , nurse , medicine.

11. feeble , month , soak.   weak , rinse , thimble.

12. knife , incision , money.   fork , cut , incisor.

In the following sentences two words need to change places so that the sentence makes sense. Underline these TWO words. Here is an example.

    She put a <u>head</u> on her <u>hat</u>.

13. He arrived with raining clothes because it was soaked.

14. When a snake sheds too big for its skin it grows it.

15. All won she of the prizes.

16. The infant school sports Monday will be held next day.

17. Untidy sergeant shouted sharply at the the soldiers.

18. The mother hen her proudly next to stood chicks.

19. Half of a hundred is five thousand.

Unjumble the letters of the word written in capital letters to make a new word which is connected with the words on either side of the brackets. Write this new word in the brackets. Here is an example.

	MALE	lunch	(*m e a l*)	dinner
20.	GIRTH	correct	(_ _ _ _ _ _)	accurate
21.	HEADS	darken	(_ _ _ _ _ _)	unlit
22.	PLUM	bulge	(_ _ _ _ _ _)	swelling
23.	PART	snare	(_ _ _ _ _ _)	catch
24.	STRESSED	sweets	(_ _ _ _ _ _)	puddings

In the following questions use THREE of the numbers on the left to complete the sum. Here is an example.

	3 , 5 , 7 , 8	16 = (*3* + *5* + *8*)
25.	8 , 9 , 12 , 19	15 = (− +)
26.	8 , 6 , 3 , 2	48 = (x x)
27.	17 , 22 , 23 , 35 , 37	50 = (+ −)
28.	3 , 4 , 5 , 6 , 7	26 = (x −)
29.	2 , 4 , 5 , 6 , 8	64 = (x x)
30.	2 , 5 , 9 , 11	15 = (+ −)

In each sentence below there is one word written in capitals which has THREE letters missing. These missing letters make a new word without changing the order of the letters. Write the new three-letter word in the brackets. Here is an example.

BUNGA*LOW*

A house with no upper floor is a BUNGA.   (LO W)

31. The gardener enjoyed looking at his FLRS.   (_ _ _ _ _)

32. There were six CHERS who taught at the school. (_ _ _ _ _)

33. The aeroplane LED on the runway.   (_ _ _ _ _)

34. She went for a HOAY at the seaside.   (_ _ _ _ _)

35. TER and Summer are two of the seasons.   (_ _ _ _ _)

36. The cowboy BRED the cow with a red hot iron.   (_ _ _ _ _)

37. Father grated the cheese with a GRR.   (_ _ _ _ _)

ONE of the words or numbers in each list is different in some way from the rest. Underline the 'odd one out'. Here is an example.

(horse , sheep , pig , cow , <u>spider</u> , goat)

38. (shoe , boot , sandal , lace , slipper , galosh)

39. (7 , 12 , 13 , 3 , 9 , 17)

40. (cornet , trombone , oboe , 'cello , clarinet , flute)

41. (bake , grill , boil , roast , beef)

42. (25 , 9 , 16 , 33 , 4 , 49)

---

43. If all varieties of zunas are a type of cactus plant and all supras are a variety of zuna, what type of plant is a supra?

(_ _ _ _ _ _ _ _)

In the following series of numbers the last two are missing. Write the missing numbers in the brackets. Here is an example.

3 , 6 , 9 , 12 , 15 , (18) , (21).

44.   3 , 6 , 12 , 24 , (_ _ _) , (_ _ _).

45.   5 , 7 , 10 , 12 , 15 , (_ _ _) , (_ _ _).

46.   4 , 5 , 7 , 10 , 14 , (_ _ _) , (_ _ _).

47.   2 , 5 , 10 , 17 , 26 , (_ _ _) , (_ _ _).

48.   6 , 10 , 8 , 12 , 10 , (_ _ _) , (_ _ _).

49.   8 , 11 , 17 , 26 , 38 , (_ _ _) , (_ _ _).

---

50. If Bob starts decorating his bedroom at 10 am and continues working for 11 hours until it is finished, at what time does he stop work?

(_ _ _ _ _ _ _)

---

51. There were four dogs who were all different ages. Fido was three years older than Scamp, but two years younger than Lassie. Chummy was two years younger than Fido. Which dog was the youngest?

(_ _ _ _ _ _ _)

In each line below there is a FOUR letter word hidden in TWO words which are next to each other. Write the hidden word in the brackets.
Here is an example.

Smi<u>le an</u>d be happy.   (*lean*)

52. The last arrival is here.   (_ _ _ _ _ _)

53. Part his hair properly.   (_ _ _ _ _ _)

54. Her hat encased her head.   (_ _ _ _ _ _)

55. The concert party returned.   (_ _ _ _ _ _)

56. Entry is by the next door.   (_ _ _ _ _ _)

57. The visitor came at six pm.   (_ _ _ _ _ _)

58. The probable debt was fifty pounds. (_ _ _ _ _ _)

In the following questions each letter stands for a number. Work out the answer to each sum and write the answer as a LETTER.

$$M = 6 , N = 2 , B = 4 , P = 5 , Q = 1.$$

59. N + P - Q = (_ _ _)

60. M - P + Q = (_ _ _)

61. M + N - P + N = (_ _ _)

In the questions below you will need to underline TWO words, one from each set of brackets, which will best complete the sentence.
Here is an example.

Sheep is to (field , <u>lamb</u> , fold) as Cow is to (farmer , milk , <u>calf</u>).

62. Music is to (note , composer , manuscript) as Story is to
                                        (adventure , cover , word).

63. Lion is to (den , mane , roar) as Mouse is to (trap , squeak , oil).

64. Claw is to (hammer , grasp , cat) as Talon is to
                                        (bicycle , eagle , screwdriver).

65. Bullet is to (fast , gun , barrel) as arrow is to (feather , shaft , bow).

66. Yellow is to (scared , grass , banana) as Red is to
                                        (sun , leaf , strawberry).

67. If harvest spiders are larger than house spiders and crane flies are larger than harvest spiders then underline which of the following statements MUST be true.

    (a) All flies are bigger than harvest spiders.

    (b) House spiders are larger than crane flies.

    (c) House spiders are often seen in houses.

    (d) Crane flies are larger than house spiders.

    (e) Harvest spiders live in barns.

The following sets of four numbers stand for FOOL, LOAF and FOAL but not necessarily in that order.

8362   8332   2368

68. Find the number code for the word ALOOF.   (_ _ _ _ _ _ _)

69. Find the number code for the word OFFAL.   (_ _ _ _ _ _ _)

70. If 5 stands for the letter T find the number code for the word AFLOAT.

    (_ _ _ _ _ _ _)

In each of the questions which follow, the three words in the group on the left of the page go together in the same way as the three words on the right. In each case the middle word of the right group is missing. Find out what this word is and write it in the brackets.
Here is an example.

        sof<u>a</u> (at) <u>t</u>in   roa<u>m</u> (*my*) <u>y</u>ou

71.   sad (lid) nil   act (_ _ _ _ _) gap

72.   sir (sin) ten   bad (_ _ _ _ _) own

73.   sty (may) ham   act (_ _ _ _ _) nib

74.   hasten (skin) knife   demist (_ _ _ _ _) arson

75.   expand (crux) truce   remote (_ _ _ _ _) windy

In the following questions you need to write in the brackets ONE letter which ends the first word in each pair and begins the second one. The SAME letter must be used in BOTH sets of brackets.
Here is an example.

SPO (*T*) APE   SHIR (*T*) RAP

76.   BEL (_ _ _) AME   TIL (_ _ _) OOM

77.   SUC (_ _ _) EEL   BOT (_ _ _) OLD

78.   SU (_ _ _) OAN   GRI (_ _ _) ESS

79.   DU (_ _ _) RIN   RUN (_ _ _) ALE

80.   GRE (_ _ _) ELP   PLA (_ _ _) OUR

81.   LOS (_ _ _) HIN   MIS (_ _ _) URE

In each question below, underline the ONE word which fits in the middle when the words are arranged in order of size or sequence.
Here is an example.

(car , coach , bicycle , rollerskate , <u>motorbike</u>)

82. (day , minute , hour , week , second)

83. (paragraph , word , sentence , letter , chapter)

84. (dinghy , liner , tug , kayak , supertanker)

85. (wren , sparrow , eagle , pigeon , ostrich)

86. (trio , quintet , duet , solo , quartet)

87. (village , country , continent , town , county)

The following number codes 427 , 742 and 246 stand for the words ALE , ELM and LEA but not necessarily in that order. Work out the code and answer these questions.

88. Find the code for the letter L.   (_ _ _)

89. Find the code for the letter M .   (_ _ _)

90. Find the code for the word MEAL.   (_ _ _ _ _)

91. What word does the code 6742 stand for?   (_ _ _ _ _ _)

In each of the following questions there should be three pairs of words. Find out what the missing word in the third pair should be and write it in the brackets. This missing word is connected with its partner in exactly the same way as with the other two pairs.
Here is an example.

pin̲t̲ , pin * wa̲r̲t̲ , war * su̲n̲k̲ , (*sun*)

92. blow , low * spit , pit * trot , (_ _ _ _)

93. vase , set * dame , met * lido , (_ _ _ _)

94. framed , ram * stoned , ton * scared , (_ _ _ _)

95. pretty , tar * drifts , far * tribal , (_ _ _ _)

96. book , cook * elan , flan * sake , (_ _ _ _)

In each of the following questions, numbers have been replaced by letters. Work out the answers to the sums and write them in the brackets. Sometimes the answers must be written as letters and sometimes as numbers.

Here is an example.

What is the answer to the following sum written as a letter?

$$H = 3 , G = 2 , Q = 7 , I = 4 , N = 9$$

$$G + H + I = (N)$$

97. Write the answer to this sum as a number.

$$G = 4 , H = 5 , I = 6 , N = 10$$

$$G + I - H = (\_\,\_)$$

98. Write the answer to this sum as a number.

$$G = 3 , H = 6 , M = 10 , I = 9 , N = 12$$

$$I - G + H = (\_\,\_)$$

99. Write the answer to this sum as a letter.

$$N = 24 , G = 5 , H = 7 , I = 11 , B = 20$$

$$H \times G - I = (\_\,\_)$$

100. Write the answer to this sum as a letter.

$$G = 100 , H = 50 , I = 25 , A = 35$$

$$G - I - H = (\_\,\_)$$

Athey Educational

Secondary Selection Portfolio

VERBAL REASONING
PAPER 14

FILL IN THE FOLLOWING INFORMATION BEFORE YOU BEGIN -

Today's Date_____

Your Surname (in capitals)_____

Your First Name(s)_____

Your Date of Birth_____

Read the following instructions carefully.

1. Start working at the beginning of the test and work straight through.
2. Answer the questions as quickly and as accurately as you can.
3. If you find you cannot answer any particular question do not spend too much time on it but move to the next one. Remember, if you finish all the questions on time you can return to any you have left out.
4. If you need to do any rough working you can use the side of the page if you wish.
5. If you need to change any of your answers do so clearly.
6. You will have 50 minutes to complete the test and you will be told the time after 20 minutes and 40 minutes.
7. Once you begin you will not be allowed to ask any questions.

TO BE COMPLETED BY THE PARENT -

PAGE	1	2	3	4	5	6	7	TOTAL
POSSIBLE	13	18	13	17	15	16	8	100
ACTUAL								

Athey Educational

In each of the following sentences there is a FOUR letter word hidden. The hidden word can be found by looking at the words next to each other in the sentence. Find the hidden word and write it in the brackets.
Here is an examples.

      The coffee i<u>s hot</u>.   (*shot*)

1.   They have stolen our money.   (_ _ _ _ _)

2.   John gave Bob all his stamps.   (_ _ _ _ _)

3.   Mary hurt both arms.   (_ _ _ _ _)

4.   Paul went to school with Anne.   (_ _ _ _ _)

5.   The balloon was full of air.   (_ _ _ _ _)

6.   Peter was in goal.   (_ _ _ _ _)

A B C D E F G H I J K L M N O P Q R S T U V W X Y Z

The above alphabet can be used to help you with some of the following questions. In each question write in the brackets either the missing numbers or the missing letters.
Here is an example.

    A , B , Z , Y , C , D , (*X*) , (*W*).

7. Z , A , Y , B , (_ _) , (_ _) , W , D.

8. I , K , M , O , (_ _ _) , (_ _ _).

9. 4 , 8 , 13 , 19 , 26 , (_ _ _) , (_ _ _) , 53.

10. E , A , F , Z , G , Y , H , (_ _ _) , (_ _ _).

11. 54 , 44 , 35 , 27 , (_ _ _) , (_ _ _) , 9.

12. A , Z , Z , C , X , X , E , V , (_ _ _) , (_ _ _).

In each of the questions below, one of the words from each group will go together to make another proper word. Remember that the word from the first group always starts the new word. Underline the TWO words, ONE from each group.
Here is an example.

    <u>any</u> / all / bone   arm / <u>body</u> / leg

13. blow / out / puff   suck / pant / in

14. rail / hand / bar	glove / train / way
15. rod / bar / in	row / out / line
16. none / some / now	when / why / how
17. think / know / mountain	edge / shelf / ledge
18. dam / young / damn	old / age / water
19. jam / bread / butter	knife / put / cup

A B C D E F G H I J K L M N O P Q R S T U V W X Y Z

The above alphabet will help you find the answers to the following code questions. Your answers should be written in the brackets.
Here is an example.

If AZKK means BALL , then BZM means (*CAN*)

20. If 1357 means ACEG , then 2468 means (_ _ _ _).

21. If KGYP means MEAN , then FCR means (_ _ _ _).

22. If OOFF means OF , then FFOOOOLL means (_ _ _ _).

23. If 16,H,14,U means PINT , then 2,D,1,E means (_ _ _ _).

24. If NAA means PEG , then RAH means (_ _ _ _).

25. If YVW means BED , then ALL means (_ _ _ _).

26. If WDST means SHOP , then GWPP means (_ _ _ _).

In each of the following questions you must underline TWO words, one from each of the groups, which have the SAME or almost the same meaning.
Here is an example.

TRY , GOAL , ATTACK .   POST , ATTEMPT , HARD .

27. PATH , WALK , SWIM .   STROLL , CRAWL , WATER .

28. ENJOY , DIFFERENT , DRINK .   LICK , SAD , LIKE .

29. LAZY , SHOOT , FIRE .   WOOD , BLAZE , GUN .

30. EVERYONE , EVERY , SOME .   NONE , EVERYBODY , TWO .

31. SING , SCHOOL , MEET .   PORK , ASSEMBLE , MEAT .

Paul's father left for work at 7.45 am. The walk to the station took 15 minutes and he usually stepped straight on a train and arrived at the office at 9.15 am. One day the train was ten minutes late and was further delayed by five minutes during the journey.

32. On this day at what time did Paul's father arrive at the office?

(_ _ _ _ _am)

33. If the walk from the station to the office normally took 15 minutes how long was the train journey when there were no delays?

(_ _ _ _mins)

In the following questions there should be three words in each group. The missing word goes with its partners in the same way as the middle word in the first group of three words goes with its partners. Write the missing word in the brackets.
Here is an example.

PULL (PAST) MAST   BENT (*BEST*) REST

34. COOK (BACK) BALL   SOOT (_ _ _ _ _) POST

35. BAT (TABLE) LEG   MUD (_ _ _ _ _) MY

36. SOWN (MOAN) MEAL   TOLD (_ _ _ _ _) CART

37. ROOF (FOOD) MELD   SOON (_ _ _ _ _) WHEN

38. BOUT (SHUT) WISH   RUSH (_ _ _ _ _) SAME

39. LOOP (PLUG) GULP   HISS (_ _ _ _ _) WOOL

40. COFFEE (COW) WICKET   DUMMY (_ _ _ _ _) TABLET

41. STORE (ROB) TABBY   FLASK (_ _ _ _ _) DADDY

Each of the following sentences has two words which should change places with each other in order to make sense. Underline BOTH of these words in each case.
Here is an example.

She put a <u>finger</u> on her <u>ring</u>.

42. Bed went straight to John.

43. Daddy got out the car and drove in the garage.

44. Can moon jump over the cows?

45. What it is in your hand?

46. We are going to by the house buy the park.

47. I like the boys on those beach.

48. Peter hoped fine weather would be the.

49. Please put your bag in the books.

In the questions below, ONE letter must be removed from the first word and placed either at the beginning or inside the second word to produce two new words. Both of these words must be real words and correctly spelt. Write BOTH new words in the brackets.
Here is an example.

BLIND and F OUR become (*BIND*) and (*FLOUR*).

50. FEUD and BOND become (_ _ _ _ _) and (_ _ _ _ _ _).

51. PATCH and RASH become (_ _ _ _ _ _) and (_ _ _ _ _ _).

52. GROW and ROUND become (_ _ _ _ _) and (_ _ _ _ _ _).

53. AWARD and WAY become (_ _ _ _ _) and (_ _ _ _ _ _).

54. QUIET and MET become (_ _ _ _ _ _) and (_ _ _ _ _ _).

55. SPLIT and PAY become (_ _ _ _ _) and (_ _ _ _ _ _).

Each of the following questions has three pairs of words. The third pair go together in the same way as the first two pairs. Complete the last pair of words by writing the missing word in the brackets.
Here is an example.

hurt - rut ; bald - lad ; mast - (*sat*)

56. emit - time ; guns - snug ; flog - (_ _ _ _ _)

57. flings - flung ; sings - sung ; sips - (_ _ _ _ _)

58. sports - stop ; traces - tear ; places - (_ _ _ _ _)

59. catch - patch ; will - pill ; host - (_ _ _ _ _)

60. fist - fish ; meat - mesh ; last - (_ _ _ _ _)

61. nine - ten ; one - two ; four - (_ _ _ _ _)

The words BALL , SOON , KITE are coded 8599 , 1337 and 2460 , but not necessarily in that order. Write down the codes for the following.

62. SKILL (_ _ _ _ _)   63. LITTLE (_ _ _ _ _)

64. STONE (_ _ _ _ _)   65. SKITTLE (_ _ _ _ _ _)

66. NOON (_ _ _ _ _)

Work out the following letter sums using the above letter values and write the answers as NUMBERS.

67. L + N + K - T = (_ _ _)

68. O x B ÷ K = (_ _ _)

69. (L - N) x B = (_ _ _)

Write the words for these number codes in the brackets.

70. 59370 (_ _ _ _ _)   71. 1492 (_ _ _ _ _)

The following table shows the marks that six children received in a series of tests. The number in the brackets is the maximum mark for that test.

	MATHS (10)	ENGLISH (20)	HISTORY (10)	SCIENCE (15)	ART (20)
John	8	12	10	13	19
Peter	7	15	9	11	13
Sarah	6	10	9	14	17
Carol	8	15	8	10	14
Tanya	3	17	8	9	15
Simon	5	13	7	15	18

Now answer the following questions.

72. How many children scored maximum marks on a test?   (_ _ _ _ _)

73. Which child scored the lowest mark on two tests?   (_ _ _ _ _)

74. How many children did better in English than in Art?   (_ _ _ _ _)

75. How many children did better in Maths than in History?   (_ _ _ _ _)

76. Who scored the highest total mark for Maths and English?   (_ _ _ _ _)

For the following questions you will need to write in the brackets ONE letter which ends the first word in each pair and begins the second one. The SAME letter must be used in BOTH sets of brackets.
Here is an example which has been done for you.

HIN (*T*) IME   TIL (*T*) ONE

77.   BIT (_ _ _) ND   TE (_ _ _) VIL

78.   BOL (_ _ _) ONE   CA (_ _ _) IVE

79.   CAL (_ _ _) OAN   FOA (_ _ _) AND

80.   INT (_ _ _) VER   HAL (_ _ _) PEN

81.   SIN (_ _ _) ONE   WIN (_ _ _) REAT

82.   BOO (_ _ _) ICK   KIC (_ _ _) ILT

83.   PAT (_ _ _) YMN   RIC (_ _ _) APPY

84.   DRES (_ _ _) HOCK   LOS (_ _ _) O

85.   SUGA (_ _ _) IGHT   TA (_ _ _) ISK

86.   WINDO (_ _ _) RITE   LO (_ _ _) ISH

In each sentence below underline TWO words, one from each set of brackets, which complete the sentence in the best way.
Here is an example.

Hat is to (<u>head</u> , bat , pig) as Shoe is to (<u>foot</u> , horse , cow).

87. Fat is to (butter , thin , huge) as Big is to (small , jam , large).

88. Build is to (house , construct , brick)
                              as Destroy is to (ship , dump , demolish).

89. Seven is to (six , one , calculate)
                              as Five is to (addition , four , ten).

90. Yellow is to (day , colour , sun)
                              as Green is to (white , grass , night).

91. Back is to (side , front , above)
                              as Bottom is to (top , down , along).

92. Pork is to (cow , goat , pig) as Beef is to (cow , goat , pig).

The following map shows the position of a school and the homes of five children, Andy (A), Betty (B), Carol (C), David (D), and Edward (E). The numbers refer to distances in metres.

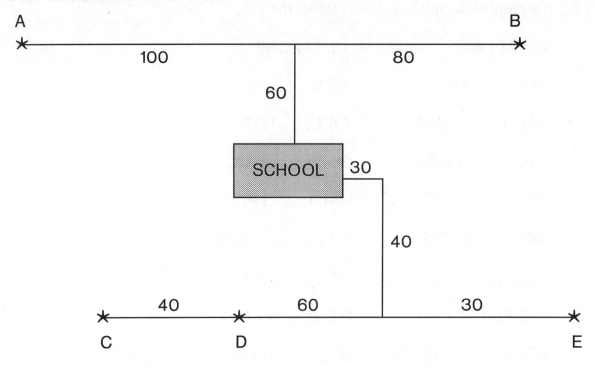

Now answer the following questions.

93. How far does Carol walk to school?   (_ _ _ _ _ m)

94. Who walks further to school, Betty or Edward?   (_ _ _ _ _ _)

95. If Edward walks to school at a speed of 1 Km in ten minutes how long does the journey take him?

    (_ _ _ _mins)

96. If Andy stays for school dinner how far are his school journeys in one week?

    (_ _ _ _ _ m)

97. One morning David called for Carol and they walked to school together. How far did David walk that morning?

    (_ _ _ _ _ m)

98. One evening after school David went straight from school to Betty's birthday party. After the party he walked home. How far did he walk altogether that evening?

    (_ _ _ _ _ m)

99. Carol also went straight from school to Betty's party. How far did she walk that evening?

    (_ _ _ _ _ m)

100. Who walks further to school, Andy or David?   (_ _ _ _ _ _)

Athey Educational

Secondary Selection Portfolio

VERBAL REASONING
PAPER 15

FILL IN THE FOLLOWING INFORMATION BEFORE YOU BEGIN -

Today's Date_____

Your Surname (in capitals)_____

Your First Name(s)_____

Your Date of Birth_____

Read the following instructions carefully.

1. Start working at the beginning of the test and work straight through.
2. Answer the questions as quickly and as accurately as you can.
3. If you find you cannot answer any particular question do not spend too much time on it but move to the next one. Remember, if you finish all the questions on time you can return to any you have left out.
4. If you need to do any rough working you can use the side of the page if you wish.
5. If you need to change any of your answers do so clearly.
6. You will have 50 minutes to complete the test and you will be told the time after 20 minutes and 40 minutes.
7. Once you begin you will not be allowed to ask any questions.

TO BE COMPLETED BY THE PARENT -

PAGE	1	2	3	4	5	6	7	TOTAL
POSSIBLE	18	11	19	14	11	15	12	100
ACTUAL								

Athey Educational

A B C D E F G H I J K L M N O P Q R S T U V W X Y Z

The above alphabet will help you to find the answers to the following code questions. Write your answers in the brackets.

1.   If PSJC means RULE, then FMJB means (_ _ _ _ _).

2.   If BQZV means COAT, then ACQP means (_ _ _ _ _).

3.   If KMLG means LOOK, then LMPP means (_ _ _ _ _).

4.   If KBW means CAT, then JJJ means (_ _ _ _ _).

5.   If DKTG means FIVE, then LKLG means (_ _ _ _ _).

The words COST , TRIP and OVER are coded 5719 , 7830 and 9024, but not necessarily in that order. Write down the codes for the following.

6.   PROVE   (_ _ _ _ _ _ _ _)

7.   CREEP   (_ _ _ _ _ _ _ _)

8.   IS IT SEPTIC?   (_ _ - _ _ - _ _ _ _ _ _ ?)

Use the above coded letters and write the answers to these sums as LETTERS.

9.   S P C   10.   O T R   11.   P V O
    + I V P   - I S S   x I
    _____   _____   _____

    _____   _____   _____

Each of the following rows has a different rule connecting the numbers. Find the rule and write the next two numbers in the brackets.

12.   2 , 1 , 4 , 3 , 6 , (_ _) , (_ _).

13.   48 , 24 , 12 , 6 , (_ _) , (_ _).

14.   150 , 120 , 90 , 60 , (_ _) , (_ _).

15.   1 , 10 , 3 , 8 , 5 , 6 , 7 , (_ _) , (_ _).

16.   0.1 , 0.4 , 0.8 , 1.3 , 1.9 , (_ _) , (_ _).

17.   2 , 4 , 5 , 7 , 8 , 10 , (_ _) , (_ _).

18.   15 , 15 , 14 , 12 , 9 , (_ _) , (_ _).

19. On a village green there are three trees, an oak, an ash and a sycamore. The sycamore is to the right of the oak. The ash is to the left of the sycamore.
    Which tree is on the far right?

    (_ _ _ _ _ _ _ _ _)

20. A supermarket carried out a cake tasting survey. Shoppers were asked to vote for their favourite cake. Cake A had less votes than cake B. Cake D had more votes than cakes C and E but less than cake A.
    Which cake was the most popular?

    (_ _ _ _ _ _ _ _ _)

21. Five boys took part in a fitness test. Tony scored higher than Sam who didn't have the lowest score. Jack had the highest score and Gerry scored more than Paul but less than Tony.
    Who had the lowest score?

    (_ _ _ _ _ _ _ _ _)

In each sentence below there is one word written in capitals which has THREE letters missing. These missing letters make a new word without changing the order of the letters. Write the new three-letter word in the brackets. Here is an example.

COM*PUT*ER
Tom played games on his COMER.   (PUT)

22. The teacher RETED the instructions for the third time.   (_ _ _ _ _)

23. After the burglary the fire HYDT was found to be damaged.   (_ _ _ _ _)

24. The JAESE capital is Tokyo.   (_ _ _ _ _)

25. The surgeon had to OPEE immediately.   (_ _ _ _ _)

Underline the word in the brackets which makes the best sense in the following sentences.

26. The orchestra played the final movement of the (sympathy , chorus , symphony , music , dance).

27. The (resident , residue , liquid , sand , oil) had formed white crystals on the bottom of the flask.

28. The doctor had given him a (prescribe , present , presentiment , prescriptive , prescription) to take to the chemist.

29. Mr Jones spoke no Russian so he asked his colleague to (interrupt , intersect , interpretation , interpret , intervene).

In each of the following questions there is one word or number which does not go with the other words or numbers in the list. Underline the 'odd one out'. Here is an example.

(coat , skirt , pullover , hair , shoes , gloves)

30. (seedling , tree , flower , bush , vegetable , beef)

31. (2 , 10 , 7 , 42 , 12 , 4 , 16)

32. (run , walk , sleep , stroll , hop , skip , kick)

33. (pig , dog , hamster , cat , butterfly , guinea pig)

34. (pencil , crayon , pen , biro , chalk , paper)

35. (brass , metal , iron , bronze , lead , aluminium)

Unjumble the word on the left and write the proper word in the brackets. Each word has some connection with the words outside the brackets.

36. LLYEWO   BLUE (_ _ _ _ _ _ _) GREEN

37. TLBTEA   FIGHT (_ _ _ _ _ _ _) SOLDIER

38. RTBASRWREY   FRUIT (_ _ _ _ _ _ _) CREAM

39. LOCKC   WATCH (_ _ _ _ _ _ _) TIME

40. IYCBLEC   PEDAL (_ _ _ _ _ _ _) HANDLEBAR

41. ALGDENN   WALES (_ _ _ _ _ _ _) SCOTLAND

42. EVSNE   SIX (_ _ _ _ _ _ _) EIGHT

In the following questions each list can be re-ordered from smallest to largest or from first to last. Underline the SMALLEST or the FIRST item in each list.

43. (July , August , June , February , December)

44. (sentence , paragraph , syllable , phrase , word)

45. (foot , head , arm , nose , leg)

46. (grape , banana , orange , grapefruit , pineapple)

47. (Saturday , Wednesday , Thursday , Friday)

48. (suitcase , handbag , trunk , briefcase , purse)

In each of the following rows there should be three pairs of words. The second word of each pair is made from the first word using the same rule for each pair. Find the rule and complete the third pair. There is a different rule for each question. Write the answer in the brackets.
Here is an example.

snow , now / show , how / slip , (lip)

49. pill , lip / wall , law / till , (_ _ _ _ _)

50. spin , win / moon , won / afar , (_ _ _ _ _)

51. nail , jail / rump , jump / petty , (_ _ _ _ _)

52. paint , pant / bound , bond / fiend , (_ _ _ _ _)

The following five words - F I S H , F O O T , F I L L , F O A M and F I N D are written in code below, but not in the same order. The same code has been used for all the words. The code for the letter S is ♯ . Write in the brackets the correct word for each code word.

53. ⋆ $ $ &   (_ _ _ _ _ _ _)

54. ⋆ ! + +   (_ _ _ _ _ _ _)

55. ⋆ ! ♯ ‹   (_ _ _ _ _ _ _)

56. ⋆ ! ? %   (_ _ _ _ _ _ _)

57. ⋆ $ £]   (_ _ _ _ _ _ _)

In each of the following sentences there is a hidden word. This FOUR letter word can be found by looking at words in the sentence which are next to each other. Find the hidden word and write it in the brackets.
Here is an example.

The bat has been broken.   (BATH)

58. John's hip was fractured.   (_ _ _ _ _ _)

59. The toy cost under ten pounds.   (_ _ _ _ _ _)

60. The team will win double points.   (_ _ _ _ _ _)

61. An adult ripped his trousers.   (_ _ _ _ _ _)

62. The pianist was playing a pleasant tune.   (_ _ _ _ _ _)

In each sentence below underline TWO words, one from each set of brackets, which complete the sentence in the best way.
Here is an example.

Him is to (male , <u>her</u> , man) as she is to (<u>he</u> , them , those).

63. Glove is to (shoe , foot , warm) as hand is to
(leg , finger , foot).

64. Bush is to (tree , brash , brush) as pint is to
(print , punt , milk).

65. Price is to (money , cost , buy) as howl is to
(hurt , bear , cry).

66. Decade is to (one , twenty , ten) as century is to
(hundred , fifty , twenty).

67. Chief is to (cowboy , indian , boss) as lord is to
(lady , castle , nobleman).

68. Mist is to (risk , missed , rain) as bust is to
(bussed , broken , rust).

69. Cow is to (grass , farmer , milk) as dog is to
(cat , meat , run).

A B C D E F G H I J K L M N O P Q R S T U V W X Y Z

The above alphabet will help you with the following questions.

70. Which letter would come before M if the alphabet was written out backwards?
(_ _ _)

71. Which letter would come between F and H if the alphabet was written out backwards?
(_ _ _)

72. Underline which of the following words would come FIRST in a dictionary?

(overcast , overcome , overhear , overcoat , overdue , overcame)

73. Write in the brackets which of the above words would come LAST in a dictionary.
(_ _ _ _ _ _ _)

In each of the questions below one word from each group will go together to make another proper word. The word from the first group always starts the new word. Underline BOTH words, ONE from each group.
Here is an example.

cut / <u>ply</u> / bush   fly / saw / <u>wood</u>

74.   play / ball / soccer   toy / boot / ground

75.   water / sea / space   yacht / ship / boat

76.   an / to / a   two / void / build

77.   throw / pitch / hurl   spoon / fork / knife

78.   a / all / an   way / some / most

79.   catch / net / trap   window / door / floor

In each of the following questions only ONE word in each set of brackets CANNOT be made by using only the letters of the word OVERTHROW.

80. (trove , worth , hew , wove , thorn)

81. (voter , throw , wrong , wrote , rove)

Each of the following questions is concerned with numbers. Work out the answer and write it in the brackets.

82. 12 is two more than half this number.   (_ _ _ _)

83. If this number is multiplied by 5 the answer is 45.   (_ _ _ _)

84. This number is five less than half of fifty.   (_ _ _ _)

85. If we multiply this number by the number of days in a week the answer is 56.

                   (_ _ _ _)

86. Halve the number of months in a year and multiply by the number in half a dozen.

                   (_ _ _ _)

87. If we add 4 to this number and then another 4 the answer is 37. (_ _ _ _)

88. Twenty is six times smaller than this number.   (_ _ _ _)

---

89. Andrew and Karen started at the same place and walked in opposite directions. Andrew walked at a speed of six kilometres an hour and Karen walked at a speed of four kilometres an hour.

ANDREW   KAREN

After they had walked for half an hour, what was the distance between them?

(_ _ _ _ _ Kms)

A B C D E F G H I J K L M N O P Q R S T U V W X Y Z

Put the following words in alphabetical order by writing the numbers 1 , 2 , 3 , 4 and 5 in the brackets.

90. sense ( ) sensation ( ) seat ( ) set ( ) sentry ( )

91. joint ( ) jog ( ) joiner ( ) joke ( ) jewel ( )

92. hang ( ) gang ( ) gander ( ) game ( ) fuss ( )

93. zoom ( ) your ( ) zero ( ) zone ( ) zigzag ( )

94. pillar ( ) pile ( ) pillow ( ) pilot ( ) pie ( )

A B C D E F G H I J K L M N O P Q R S T U V W X Y Z

The above alphabet will help you to find the rule which connects each of the letters in the following rows. There is a different rule for each row. Find the rule and write the missing letter in the brackets.

95.   B , D , F , H , (_ _ _) .

96.   M , L , (_ _ _) , G , C .

97.   Z , A , (_ _ _) , B , X .

98.   N , O , M , (_ _ _) , L .

99.   Z , X , (_ _ _) , T , R .

100.   E , F , H , K , (_ _ _) .

Athey Educational

Secondary Selection Portfolio

VERBAL REASONING
PAPER 16

FILL IN THE FOLLOWING INFORMATION BEFORE YOU BEGIN -

Today's Date_____

Your Surname (in capitals)_____

Your First Name(s)_____

Your Date of Birth_____

Read the following instructions carefully.

1. Start working at the beginning of the test and work straight through.
2. Answer the questions as quickly and as accurately as you can.
3. If you find you cannot answer any particular question do not spend too much time on it but move to the next one. Remember, if you finish all the questions on time you can return to any you have left out.
4. If you need to do any rough working you can use the side of the page if you wish.
5. If you need to change any of your answers do so clearly.
6. You will have 50 minutes to complete the test and you will be told the time after 20 minutes and 40 minutes.
7. Once you begin you will not be allowed to ask any questions.

TO BE COMPLETED BY THE PARENT -

PAGE	1	2	3	4	5	6	7	TOTAL
POSSIBLE	13	11	16	18	16	13	13	100
ACTUAL								

Athey Educational

In each of the following questions underline TWO words, numbers or sets of letters which do not belong with the rest.
Here is an example.

(cat , rabbit , <u>daffodil</u> , dog , <u>dandelion</u>)

1. (ab , fg , km , cd , yz , rt)

2. (diamond , clay , ruby , emerald , resin , sapphire)

3. (313 , 424 , 626 , 727 , 818 , 929)

4. (wrestling , play , boxing , tennis , bat , football)

5. (trunk , case , label , satchel , knapsack , van)

In each of the following sets of brackets, underline the TWO words which are connected in some way with the words written in capital letters.
Here is an example.

RED YELLOW　　(fur , leg , <u>blue</u> , coat , <u>green</u>)

6. TIGER LEOPARD (lizard , horse , cheetah , frog , lion , hedgehog)

7. HUGE MASSIVE (whale , elephant , gigantic , fierce , odd , colossal)

8. BOOT SHOE (foot , sandal , stocking , laces , sole , slipper)

9. PECULIAR ODD (strange , even , poverty , vagrant , unusual , hermit)

10. MAHOGANY OAK (wood , pine , teak , hammer , cabinet , screwdriver)

In the following questions underline the correct answers.

11. Peter likes peas and carrots. His father likes carrots and beans. His mother likes peas, carrots and beans. What would be the best vegetable to provide for all of them?

(peas , carrots , beans)

12. If things which had no colour were always more valuable than things which had a colour, which of these would be the most valuable?

(gold , silver , copper , water , brass , bronze)

13. In two years time my father will be exactly three times as old as I am now. My father is now thirty-seven. How old am I?

(13 , 14 , 15 , 12 , 16 , 17)

A B C D E F G H I J K L M N O P Q R S T U V W X Y Z

The following questions contain a series of letter pairs. Work out the missing pair of letters and write them in the brackets. Use the above alphabet to help you.
Here is an example.

AB , CD , EF , (*GH*) , IJ , KL .

14. FR , HR , JR , (_ _ _) , NR , PR .

15. (_ _ _ _) , CD , DE , EF , FG , GH .

16. HA , (_ _ _ _) , JC , KD , LE , MF .

17. YZ , WX , UV , ST , (_ _ _ _) , OP .

18. BA , DC , FE , HG , JI , (_ _ _ _) .

The following questions have words written in code. Each question has a different code. Underline the correct answers in the brackets.
Here is an example.

If <u>457</u>286 means <u>THI</u>NGS, what does 574 mean?

(sin , <u>hit</u> , gin , tin , sit)

19. If 2534798 means MONSTER, what does 8947 mean?

(stem , must , rest , most , rent)

20. If 369821 means FORGET, what does 861 mean?

(rot , got , get , rug , for)

21. If 248913 means FASTER, what does 8421 mean?

(east , test , safe , seat , fate)

22. If 72316435 means CONTAINS, what does 51261 mean?

(stoat , stint , coats , stain , taint)

23. If 51643521 means RESOURCE, what does 2351 mean?

(sour , cure , seer , curt , rose)

24. If 5836247 means PLAINER, what does 8432 mean?

(near, rain , lean , pale, line)

The five words DAILY , AISLE , SAILS , DIARY and SLIDE are written in code below. Write the word which stands for each code in the brackets.

25.   *   £   =   ›   %   (_ _ _ _ _ _ _)

26.   =   £   ?   &   +   (_ _ _ _ _ _ _)

27.   *   =   £   &   %   (_ _ _ _ _ _ _)

28.   ?   =   £   &   ?   (_ _ _ _ _ _ _)

29.   ?   &   £   *   +   (_ _ _ _ _ _ _)

In each of the following sentences underline the word in brackets which makes the best sense. Here is an example.

  Dog is to puppy as cat is to (pet , animal , <u>kitten</u> , baby).

30. Bread is to flour as butter is to (cheese , flower , cream , bread , dish).

31. Twelve is to dozen as pair is to (score , fruit , twenty , two , trousers).

32. Flower is to flour as sun is to (moon , son , planet , sky , earth).

33. Aunt is to niece as uncle is to (boy , girl , sister , nephew , brother).

34. Rood is to door as room is to (door , ceiling , window , house , moor).

35. Fish is to fin as bird is to (sky , feather , scales , wing , nest).

Five shops were named A, B, C, D and E. C sold vegetables and groceries. A and D sold only groceries. The others only sold vegetables. A and B had only two assistants. The others had three. C and E were self-service shops but the others were not. Now underline the correct answers to the following questions.

36. Which shop was not self-service and had three
  sales assistants?   (A , B , C , D , E)

37. Which self-service shop sold only vegetables?   (A , B , C , D , E)

38. Which shop was not self-service, sold vegetables
  and had two sales assistants?   (A , B , C , D , E)

39. Which shop was not self-service, sold only
  groceries and had two sales assistants?   (A , B , C , D , E)

40. Which self-service shop sold vegetables
  and groceries?   (A , B , C , D , E)

Complete the following number series by filling in the blank spaces.

41.   1 , 5 , 9 , (_ _ _) , (_ _ _) , 21 , 25 .

42.   (_ _ _) , 6 , 9 , (_ _ _) , 15 , 18 , 21 .

43.   30 , 24 , 19 , 15 , (_ _ _) , (_ _ _) , 9 .

44.   81 , 64 , 49 , (_ _ _) , 25 , (_ _ _) .

45.   2 , 1 , 4 , 2 , 6 , (_ _ _) , (_ _ _) .

46.   20 , 1 , 19 , 2 , (_ _ _) , (_ _ _) , 17 .

47.   (_ _ _) , 5 , 8 , 13 , 20 , 29 , (_ _ _) .

Underline ONE word which can be made using the letters of the word in capitals.

48. PROBLEM   (moles , open , parole , probe , robes)

49. ADMIRE   (harm , raid , more , arms , bead)

50. SOLDIER   (reins , lost , loins , rose , road)

51. PRACTICE   (actor , trace , prices , rapture , place)

52. DUNGEON   (engine , dunes , nudge , gnome , under)

53. VALUABLE   (valve , label , beam , bales , blame)

A B C D E F G H I J K L M N O P Q R S T U V W X Y Z

The above alphabet is to help you with the following questions.

54. Which letter is exactly half way between the seventh and the thirteenth letter of the alphabet?   (_ _ _)

55. Which letter in the seventh month of the year comes earliest in the alphabet?   (_ _ _)

56. Which letter comes between L and Q in the alphabet and cannot be found in the word PHONE?   (_ _ _)

57. If the letter T comes later in the alphabet than the fourth letter of the first month of the year, write X in the brackets. If it does not then write A.

          (_ _ _)

58. Which letter of the day of the week which starts with the letter nearest to the end of the alphabet is nearest to the letter C ?   (_ _ _)

Each of the following questions contains groups of words. There are TWO 'odd ones out' in each group of words. Underline the two words which do not belong with the others.
Here is an example for you.

MARY , WENDY , <u>GIRL</u> , SALLY , <u>SKIRT</u> , DEBORAH .

59. HOT , TEPID , WATER , LUKEWARM , SCORCHING , KETTLE .

60. CUNNING , SLY , CRAFTY , THIEF , WILY , SNEAK .

61. BIRCH , BUTTERCUP , FIR , SNOWDROP , PINE , ELM .

62. SKY , CLOUD , MARS , MERCURY , VENUS , JUPITER .

63. ORANGE , APPLE , PEAR , PEACH , CUCUMBER , RADISH .

64. WATCH , CLOCK , STARE , LOOK , HAND , GLANCE .

In the table below there are six groups of words. The groups are labelled 1, 2, 3, 4, 5 and 6. Each group contains words which are connected with each other in some way.

1	2	3	4	5	6
walk	hit	speak	scowl	imitation	bumper
run	smack	whisper	blush	copy	tyre
stroll	blow	yell	grin	fake	wheel

Now place the following words in the correct group by writing the correct number in the brackets next to each one.

Here is an example.   duplicate   (5)

65. thump   (_ _ _)   66. talk   (_ _ _)

67. windscreen   (_ _ _)   68. sprint   (_ _ _)

69. leer   (_ _ _)   70. counterfeit   (_ _ _)

71. forgery   (_ _ _)   72. shout   (_ _ _)

73. trot   (_ _ _)   74. strike   (_ _ _)

A B C D E F G H I J K L M N O P Q R S T U V W X Y Z

In the letter series below write the next two letters or pairs of letters in the brackets. The alphabet above will help you.

75. B , F , J , (_ _ _) , (_ _ _).

76. C , H , M , (_ _ _) , (_ _ _).

77. WV , VU , UT , (_ _ _) , (_ _ _).

78. AD , BE , CF , (_ _ _) , (_ _ _).

79. OP , NQ , MR , (_ _ _) , (_ _ _).

80. FA , HD , JG , (_ _ _) , (_ _ _).

A = 1 E = 2 R = 3 S = 5 T = 10

Now answer the following questions.

81. Add together the letters of the word EAST and write the answer as a number.

(_ _ _ _)

82. Total the letters of the word TASTER and write the answer as a number.

(_ _ _ _)

83. Multiply all the letters of the word SEA together and write the answer as a LETTER.

(_ _ _ _)

84. Multiply the first three letters of the word RATS together and divide the answer by the last letter. Write the answer as a number.

(_ _ _ _)

---

85. How many letters occur more than once in the word PHENOMENON?

(_ _ _)

86. Which letter occurs twice in AMUSEMENT, twice in PLEASURE and only once in PROBABLE?

(_ _ _)

87. If all the letters of the word ACRIMONIOUS were placed in alphabetical order which one would come third?

(_ _ _)

In each of the next questions you need to underline TWO words. One of these words must be the opposite of and the other have the same meaning as the word written in capital letters.
Here is an example.

HAPPY (small , <u>sad</u> , mouse , <u>joyful</u> , ground)

88. WEAK (day , hour , powerful , tired , feeble , giant)

89. SCATTER (run , hide , disperse , gather , control , disguise)

90. MANY (all , more , numerous , often , few , none)

91. FEROCIOUS (excited , lion , meek , dove , calm , fierce)

92. DAMAGE (made , help , hammer , mischief , repair , injure)

93. RAISE (current , elevate , platform , wage , lower , salary)

In each of the following sentences one word has its letters jumbled. Put the letters of each word in the right order and write it in the brackets.

94. A W O W N I D is for looking through. (_ _ _ _ _ _ _)

95. Acting is seen at the R E E T A T H. (_ _ _ _ _ _ _)

96. A B U R E C M C U is eaten with salad. (_ _ _ _ _ _ _)

The following three words are connected with each other.

COMB
COM**E**
HOME

Each of the first two words has had ONE letter changed to make it into a new word. COMB has been made into COME by changing the B to E, and COME has been made into HOME by changing the C to H.

The following groups of words have the middle word missing. Work out what each word is and write it on the line of dots.

97. R E A R   98. S A L E   99. M I N E   100. P E S T

. . . .

N E A T   T A L C   M O L E   P A C T

Secondary Selection Portfolio

VERBAL REASONING
PAPER 17

FILL IN THE FOLLOWING INFORMATION BEFORE YOU BEGIN -

Today's Date_____

Your Surname (in capitals)_____

Your First Name(s)_____

Your Date of Birth_____

Read the following instructions carefully.

1. Start working at the beginning of the test and work straight through.
2. Answer the questions as quickly and as accurately as you can.
3. If you find you cannot answer any particular question do not spend too much time on it but move to the next one. Remember, if you finish all the questions on time you can return to any you have left out.
4. If you need to do any rough working you can use the side of the page if you wish.
5. If you need to change any of your answers do so clearly.
6. You will have 50 minutes to complete the test and you will be told the time after 20 minutes and 40 minutes.
7. Once you begin you will not be allowed to ask any questions.

TO BE COMPLETED BY THE PARENT -

PAGE	1	2	3	4	5	6	7	TOTAL
POSSIBLE	15	17	15	14	10	16	13	100
ACTUAL								

Athey Educational

A B C D E F G H I J K L M N O P Q R S T U V W X Y Z

The above alphabet is to help you with the following code questions. Each line uses a different code. Write the answers in the brackets.

1.   If GNMDX stands for HONEY, then ADD means (_ _ _ _ _ _).

2.   If CTPVIGS stands for BROTHER, then GCSVIGS means (_ _ _ _ _ _).

3.   If YFGGVI stands for BUTTER, then YFGGVIUOB means (_ _ _ _ _ _).

4.   If BIN stands for HOT, then NLCWE stands for (_ _ _ _ _ _).

In each of the following lines there are TWO words which are similar to each other but different from the rest. Underline these TWO words in each set of brackets.
Here is an example.

(buy , <u>repay</u> , shop , <u>refund</u> , money , pound)

5.   (thirsty , empty , parched , water , swim , smooth)

6.   (gun , fight , shoot , cowboy , horse , brawl)

7.   (leisurely , fun , park , slowly , quickly , slide)

8.   (two , to , too , trio , all , also)

In the following sentences one of the words has its letters jumbled up. Unjumble the letters and write the word, properly spelt, in the brackets. Here is an example.

VRSTEII means to go again.   (*REVISIT*)

9.   STREEDDOY means ruined.   (_ _ _ _ _ _ _ _ _)

10.   FEELSILS means dead.   (_ _ _ _ _ _ _ _)

11.   MOBOUTAEIL is another word for car.   (_ _ _ _ _ _ _ _ _ _)

12.   A HYOUT is a young man.   (_ _ _ _ _ _ _)

13.   A RAMP is like a cot on wheels.   (_ _ _ _ _ _ _)

14.   BUMLEJ is a lot of letters all mixed up. (_ _ _ _ _ _)

15.   A GANF is a long, sharp tooth.   (_ _ _ _ _ _ _)

In the following questions the first two words go together in the same way as the third word goes with one that is missing. The number after the brackets tells you how many letters there are in the missing word.

16. knife , cut   *   spade , (_ _ _ _ _ _ _) 3

17. big , biggest   *   good , (_ _ _ _ _ _ _) 4

18. pigs , trotter   *   horses , (_ _ _ _ _ _ _) 4

19. smile , happy   *   frown , (_ _ _ _ _ _ _) 3

20. three , four   *   double , (_ _ _ _ _ _ _) 6

In each of the following underline the ONE word which means EITHER the same as or the opposite of the word written in capitals.

21. SOILED   (garden , clean , plant , walk , lubricated)

22. SOLID   (hard , shape , hollow , soft , cube , bought)

23. FLOWER   (rose , petals , propagate , ground , bloom)

24. NEED   (dough , require , cook , deed , kneed)

25. BRILLIANT   (colour , blue , bright , yellow , sun)

In each of the sentences below TWO of the words have changed places. Underline BOTH words which need to change places so that the sentence makes sense. Here is an example.

John <u>with</u> to the park <u>went</u> his mother.

26. Thirty five and twenty one make fifty four.

27. Spiders in small insects catch their web.

28. We eight ate cakes for tea.

29. The postman bit the dog.

30. John's sister was his mother's aunt.

31. The smoke went into the chimney and up the sky.

---

32. If each of the names of the months of the year had the two letters nearest to the beginning of the alphabet removed, what would be the fourth letter of the eighth month of the year?

(_ _ _ _ _)

In each of the following questions select numbers from the left hand side of the page and write them in the brackets in order to make the number you are given. One of the numbers must be used TWICE.
Here is an example.

	2, 3, 5, 8	:	18 = (*3* x *5* + *3*)
33.	4, 9, 10, 13, 25	:	7 = (- -)
34.	3, 4, 8, 9, 10	:	27 = (x +)
35.	2, 3, 5, 20, 30	:	7 = (÷ -)
36.	2, 4, 7, 9, 16	:	60 = (x -)
37.	3, 5, 6, 9, 10	:	108 = (x x)
38.	4, 7, 8, 16, 25	:	5 = (+ ÷)

In each of the following questions ONE letter must be taken from the word on the left and placed into or added to the word on the right so that both new words are proper words which are correctly spelt. All the other letters must remain in the same order.

39. CHARM and AT become (_ _ _ _ _ _) and (_ _ _ _ _ _).

40. COUNTRY and USE become (_ _ _ _ _ _) and (_ _ _ _ _ _).

41. TRAIN and SAG become (_ _ _ _ _ _) and (_ _ _ _ _ _).

42. BRACE and EAT become (_ _ _ _ _ _) and (_ _ _ _ _ _).

43. ROAM and MAT become (_ _ _ _ _ _) and (_ _ _ _ _ _).

44. MISERY and OUR become (_ _ _ _ _ _) and (_ _ _ _ _ _).

In the following lines there are two groups of three words. The three words on the right hand side of the page go together in the same way as the three words on the left. The middle word of the group on the right is missing. Write the missing word in the brackets.
Here is an example.

	PA<u>IN</u> (INTO) <u>TO</u>OL	*	MI<u>ST</u> (*STUN*) <u>UN</u>DO
45.	FALL (SWILL) WISH	*	BUST (_ _ _ _ _ _) OARS
46.	FOOT (ROOT) ROOM	*	LIST (_ _ _ _ _ _) FIND
47.	PEST (TRUE) TURN	*	TYRE (_ _ _ _ _ _ _) PALM

48. SOAP (ROSE) LURE   *   LURE (_ _ _ _ _ _) TASK

49. DOME (COME) HOME   *   DASH (_ _ _ _ _ _) HASH

50. IN (INTO) TO   *   OUT (_ _ _ _ _ _) SIDE

In a secret code the word WINKUMB stands for LEOTARD. Using the same code work out how the following words would be written.

51. DOOR   (_ _ _ _ _ _ _ _ _)

52. LATE   (_ _ _ _ _ _ _ _ _)

53. TOAD   (_ _ _ _ _ _ _ _ _)

54. LETTER   (_ _ _ _ _ _ _ _ _)

Using the same code work out what the following code words stand for.

55. KMIUB   (_ _ _ _ _ _ _ _ _)

56. BUMI   (_ _ _ _ _ _ _ _ _)

57. BN-U-WNK   (_ _ - _ _ - _ _ _ _)

---

58. When Daren was five his father gave him 10 pence pocket money each week. For three years his pocket money was increased each year by 10 pence and then for two years it was increased each year by 15 pence. It was then doubled each year for four years. How much pocket money did his father give him when Daren was fourteen years of age?

(£ _ _ _ _ _)

In the following three words the first word has been made into the last word by changing one letter at each step so that a proper word is still there at each stage.

L O O K
L O C K
S O C K

Using the same rule write the middle word of each of the following groups of three.

59. F I S H   60. H O L D   61. S M A R T

....

W I S E   M O O D   S T A R K

Use the following bus timetable to answer the questions. All buses start from Porttown and finish their journey at Febworth. You will notice that some of the buses are expresses and only stop at the larger villages.

Destination	Morning			Afternoon		
Porttown	7.15	8.15	10.15	12.05	14.15	17.15
Craston			10.25	12.15	14.25	
Oldster	7.30	8.30	10.35	12.25	14.35	17.30
Littleham			10.55	12.45	14.55	
Bigham	7.55	8.55	11.10	13.00	15.10	17.55
Thornley	8.10	9.10	11.25	13.15	15.25	18.10
Febworth	8.20	9.20	11.35	13.25	15.35	18.20

62. At what time would you leave Craston to arrive at Thornley at 15.25?

(_ _ _ _ _ _ _)

63. How long does the journey from Porttown to Febworth take when the bus stops at each village on the route?

(_ _ _hrs _ _ _mins)

64. What time did the bus leave Porttown if it arrived at Thornley at ten past nine in the morning?

(_ _ _ _ _ _ _)

65. How much quicker is the journey from Porttown to Febworth when passengers travel by one of the express buses?

(_ _ _ _ _mins)

66. How many times each day do buses stop at Littleham? (_ _ _ _ _times)

67. Mrs Jones left Craston for Thornley at 10.25 am but stopped at Oldster to see a friend and caught the next bus. How long did she stay in Oldster?

(_ _ _hrs _ _ _mins)

68. When did Mrs Jones arrive at Thornley? (_ _ _ _ _ _ _)

69. If Jane arrived at the bus stop in Porttown at 5.30 in the afternoon, had she missed the last bus to Febworth or not? (YES or NO)

(_ _ _ _ _ _ _)

70. John lived in Littleham and arranged to meet a friend at Thornley at 11.30 am. At what time did he catch a bus from home?

(_ _ _ _ _ _ _)

71. Mr. Brown lives in Oldster and works in Bigham from Monday to Friday. If he travelled to work by the earliest express bus and the return journey took exactly the same amount of time, how much time did he spend travelling on the bus every week?

(_ _ _ _ _mins)

In the following you will need to underline ONE item from each set of brackets in order to make the sentence into one that makes the most sense.

72. The (policeman , postman , doctor) arrested the (dog , thief , patient) as he left the (bank , letter , boot).

73. When (wood , bread , water) is heated it (boils , toast, burns) and gives off (burnt , steam , water).

74. (When , Which , There) train leaves (Room , Platform , Station) Four at (4pm , Tuesday , April)?

75. (The , Them , There) (boy , was , then) (and , the , ran) across the road.

The following questions are a series of numbers. Work out the missing number.

76.   1 ,   11 ,   20 ,   28 ,   35 ,   (_ _ _ _)

77.   81 ,   64 ,   49 ,   36 ,   25 ,   (_ _ _ _)

78.   10 ,   -9 ,   8 ,   -7 ,   6 ,   (_ _ _ _)

79.   8 ,   11 ,   16 ,   23 ,   32 ,   (_ _ _ _)

80.   748 ,   657 ,   566 ,   475 ,   384 ,   (_ _ _ _)

A B C D E F G H I J K L M N O P Q R S T U V W X Y Z

Complete the following letter sequences by writing the next letter or set of letters in the brackets. There is a different rule governing each sequence.

81. ZY ,   XX ,   VW ,   TV ,   (_ _ _)

82. ABC ,   CBF ,   EBI ,   GBL ,   (_ _ _)

83. A , Y , C , W , E , U , G , (_ _ _)

84. S , Q , N , J , (_ _ _)

In each of the following questions TWO words in each set of brackets CANNOT be made from the letters of the word in capitals. Underline these TWO word.

85. MARMALADE   (dare / deal / leer / meal / made / late)

86. HURRICANE   (rich / rain / hive / rice / hear / vane)

87. DESCEND   (deep / need / seed / deed / seen / feed)

88. CHAUFFEUR (fear / hear / rear / fuse / ruff / cuff)

89. INVISIBLE (live / tile / vile / pine / line / bile)

In the following questions underline the right answer.

90. Which of the following would come FIRST in a dictionary?

(flight , flew , flesh , flea , fling)

91. Which of the following would come SECOND in a dictionary?

(spot , spool , spoil , sport , sponge)

92. Which of the following would come THIRD in a dictionary?

(victory , vicar , visible , vine , vigour)

93. Which of the following would come FOURTH in a dictionary?

(vein , nutmeg , keep , keel , keen)

94. Which of the following would come FIFTH in a dictionary?

(attack , attach , ash , auction , aunt)

95. Which word can be made from the letters MRTOONYSA ?

(astronaut , astonish , astronomer , astronomy)

96. Which word can be made from the letters ECEXTP ?

(expand , expert , explain , expect , explore)

97. Which jumbled word is MARBLE ?   (blreem , raablm , marled , blearm)

A B C D E F G H I J K L M N O P Q R S T U V W X Y Z

98. Which letter in the alphabet follows the letter which can be found most frequently in the word CASTAWAY?

(_ _ _)

99. What is the fourth letter of the month of the year whose first letter is between N and S in the alphabet?

(_ _ _)

100. Which letter is twice the distance from the end of the alphabet as D is from the beginning?

(_ _ _)

 Athey Educational

Secondary Selection Portfolio

VERBAL REASONING
PAPER 18

FILL IN THE FOLLOWING INFORMATION BEFORE YOU BEGIN -

Today's Date_____

Your Surname (in capitals)_____

Your First Name(s)_____

Your Date of Birth_____

Read the following instructions carefully.

1. Start working at the beginning of the test and work straight through.
2. Answer the questions as quickly and as accurately as you can.
3. If you find you cannot answer any particular question do not spend too much time on it but move to the next one. Remember, if you finish all the questions on time you can return to any you have left out.
4. If you need to do any rough working you can use the side of the page if you wish.
5. If you need to change any of your answers do so clearly.
6. You will have 50 minutes to complete the test and you will be told the time after 20 minutes and 40 minutes.
7. Once you begin you will not be allowed to ask any questions.

TO BE COMPLETED BY THE PARENT -

PAGE	1	2	3	4	5	6	7	TOTAL
POSSIBLE	18	19	17	14	12	7	13	100
ACTUAL								

Athey Educational

In each sentence there are two words which need to change places so that the sentence makes sense. Underline BOTH words.

1. Swiftly dolphin swam the in the sea.

2. There in one thousand grammes are a kilogramme.

3. It is unusual to a able to see be fox.

4. She broke down the hill and fell her leg.

5. Most leaves fall from autumn trees during the.

6. He knew the air so he raised his hand in the answer.

7. You need flour make yeast to and bread.

8. The spider fly the caught in its web.

In each question below, one word from each group will go together to make another proper word. The word from the first group always starts the new word. Underline the TWO words, ONE from each group. Here is an example.

floor / <u>wall</u> / table   small / roof / <u>paper</u>

9.   day / week / road   lap / end / sat

10.   not / pencil / thick   pen / thin / ice

11.   all / most / every   end / where / fast

12.   cart / tree / branch   soap / wood / on

13.   is / be / at   top / hind / son

14.   bat / not / tab   when / or / let

In each of the following sentences there is a FOUR letter word hidden. The hidden word can be found by looking at words in the sentence next to each other. Find the hidden word and write it in the brackets. Here is an example.

The cal<u>m end</u>ed quickly.   (*mend*)

15. Curry is a blend of spices.   (_ _ _ _ _ _ _)

16. Most operations are routine.   (_ _ _ _ _ _ _)

17. Sports cars are expensive.   (_ _ _ _ _ _ _)

18. They like to ski down slopes.   (_ _ _ _ _ _ _)

---

seal lash hale

The words HALE , SEAL , LASH are coded 5842 , 2453 and 3428 but not necessarily in that order. Write down the codes for the following.

19. SHELL   (_ _ _ _ _ _ _ _)

20. ALES   (_ _ _ _ _ _ _ _)

21. LEASH   (_ _ _ _ _ _ _ _)

22. HEALS   (_ _ _ _ _ _ _ _)

Work out the following letter sums using the above letter values.

23. (A x E) + L =   (_ _ _)   Write the answer as a *number.*

24. (E + L) ÷ S =   (_ _ _)   Write the answer as a *letter.*

25. (A + S) ÷ H =   (_ _ _)   Write the answer as a *letter.*

26. S + E + H + A = (_ _ _)   Write the answer as a *number.*

27. (2 x E) – L =   (_ _ _)   Write the answer as a *number.*

In each of the following questions there is one word which does not go with the other words in the list. Underline the 'odd one out'. Here is an example.

     (coat , skirt , pullover , <u>hair</u> , shoes , gloves)

28. (pear , apricot , sprout , peach , apple , orange)

29. (lemonade , gin , whisky , brandy , rum , liqueur)

30. (France , Holland , Amsterdam , Denmark , England)

31. (clay , lawn , peat , silt , loam)

32. (king , prince , queen , lord , duke , earl)

Unjumble the following words and write the proper word in the brackets. This word has some connection with the word on either side of the brackets.

33.   GUEFD   SWEET (_ _ _ _ _ _ _ _) TOFFEE

34.   CIKTS   GLUE   (_ _ _ _ _ _ _ _) PASTE

35.   KLEAN   ELBOW (_ _ _ _ _ _ _ _) KNEE

36.   SELML   ODOUR (_ _ _ _ _ _ _ _) AROMA

37.   LIMES   GRIN   (_ _ _ _ _ _ _ _) LAUGH

In the following questions, each list can be reordered from smallest to largest or from first to last. Underline the SMALLEST or the FIRST item in each list.

38. (grape , pineapple , water melon , peach , grapefruit)

39. (potato , cauliflower , pea , mushroom , onion)

40. (village , country , hamlet , town , county)

41. (four , fourteen , fifty , twenty-one , seven)

42. (duet , quintet , trio , solo , quartet , octet)

43. (rat , kangaroo , rabbit , badger , mouse)

44. (youth , child , adult , toddler , baby)

45. (tennis ball , football , golf ball , marble , bowl)

Each of the following questions is concerned with numbers. Work out the answer and write it in the brackets.

46. 10 is one more than half this number. (_ _ _)

47. If you add six to this number and subtract nine the answer is 17. (_ _ _)

48. This number is ten less than half of a hundred. (_ _ _)

49. If we multiply this number by the number of sides in a triangle the answer is 60.

(_ _ _)

50. This number is double the number of months in a year added to half a century.

(_ _ _)

51. If we add 9 to this number and then another 9 the answer is 43. (_ _ _)

52. Ten is twenty times smaller than this number. (_ _ _)

A B C D E F G H I J K L M N O P Q R S T U V W X Y Z

Put the following words in alphabetical order by writing the numbers 1 , 2 , 3 , 4 and 5 in the brackets.

53. motor ( )   mother ( )   motive ( )   monk ( )   motion ( )

54. fire ( )   fig ( )   figure ( )   fight ( )   fifth ( )

55. digger ( ) dinghy ( ) dim ( ) dime ( ) digit ( )

56. fake ( ) fall ( ) faith ( ) fail ( ) facet ( )

57. great ( ) grand ( ) grebe ( ) group ( ) grit ( )

In each question below, underline the ONE word which fits in the middle when the words are arranged in order of size or sequence.
Here is an example.

(car , coach , bicycle , roller skate , <u>motorbike</u>)

58. (day , year , month , week , century)

59. (thimble , bucket , jug , cup , bath)

60. (August , October , March , December , February)

61. (fifteenth , ninth , twentieth , second , first)

The following number codes stand for the words PEAT, PATH and HATE but not necessarily in that order.

9 2 5 6   6 2 5 8   9 8 2 5

Work out the code and answer these questions.

62. Find the code for the word TAPE.   (_ _ _ _ _ _)

63. Find the code for the word THAT.   (_ _ _ _ _ _)

64. What word does the code 6829 stand for? (_ _ _ _ _ _)

In the following questions TWO of the words are 'odd ones out'. Underline the two words which do not belong with the others.
Here is an example.

MARY , WENDY , <u>GIRL</u> , SALLY , <u>SKIRT</u> , DEBORAH .

65. OPPOSE , DEFY , EMOTION , RESIST , ANGER , DISSENT.

66. NEGLIGENT , SAD , THOUGHTLESS , CARELESS , NAUGHTY , REMISS.

67. SHOE , SOLE , SANDAL , LEATHER , BOOT , SLIPPER.

68. ATLANTIC , PACIFIC , SEA , OCEAN , INDIAN , MEDITERRANEAN.

In each of the next questions you need to underline TWO words. One of these words must be the opposite of the word written in capital letters and the other have the same meaning. Here is an example.

HAPPY (small , <u>sad</u> , mouse , <u>joyful</u> , ground)

69. SATISFIED (sad , displeased , full , feeble , contented)

70. BEAUTIFUL (good , cute , ugly , pretty , popular , girl)

71. LAZY (sluggish , miserable , idiot , fast , active , work)

72. CLEVER (brain , idle , stupid , teacher , top , intelligent)

A B C D E F G H I J K L M N O P Q R S T U V W X Y Z

The above alphabet is to help you with the following code questions. Each line has a different code. Write the answers in the brackets.

73. If QBSUZ stands for PARTY, then TBOE means (_ _ _ _ _ _).

74. If QGBC stands for SIDE, then DGR means (_ _ _ _ _ _).

75. If FZQCDM stands for GARDEN, then GNKC means (_ _ _ _ _ _).

76. If WDS stands for TAP, then KLW stands for (_ _ _ _ _ _).

---

77. If there are more letters in DISCONCERTED than there are in FAVOURITE underline X, unless there are less letters in COMPUTER than in ANNIVERSARY, in which case you should underline Y.

(X Y)

78. If all the days of the week were arranged in alphabetical order, which would come first?

(_ _ _ _ _ _ _ _)

---

79. My watch is twelve minutes slow. The bus for which I am waiting should have arrived at 3.49 pm but it is five minutes late. What time would my watch show when the bus arrives?

(_ _ _ _ _ _ pm)

80. Deborah's father is twice as old as she is now. If their ages add up to 45 years, how old is Deborah?

(_ _ _ _ _ _ _ yrs)

At the start of the season the members of Heaton United Football Team decided to try to score more than thirty goals and have less than fifteen scored against them in their first fifteen games. Graph 1 shows how many goals were scored against them in each of these 15 games. Graph 2 shows how many goals they scored in these games. Each of the matches is labelled M1, M2, M3 etc . . . up to M15.

GRAPH 1. GOALS SCORED AGAINST HEATON UNITED

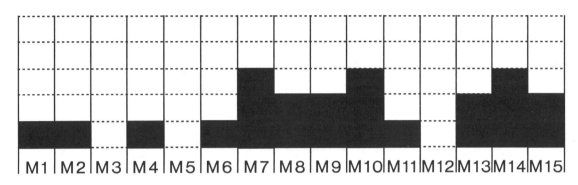

GRAPH 2. GOALS SCORED FOR HEATON UNITED

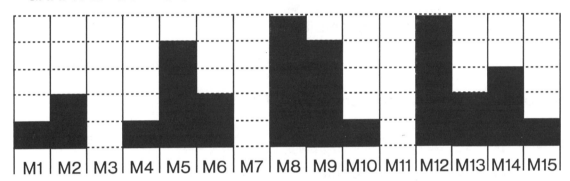

Now answer the following questions.

81.   Circle how many matches were drawn.   (0 , 1 , 2 , 3 , 4 , 5 , 6)

82.   How many matches did they win?   (0 , 1 , 2 , 3 , 4 , 5 , 6)

83.   How many games did they lose?   (0 , 1 , 2 , 3 , 4 , 5 , 6)

84.   Did they score a total of more than 30 goals?   (Yes / No)

85.   Were less than 15 goals scored against them?   (Yes / No)

86.   Which was the highest scoring match?   (M_ _ _)

87.   Which match was a goalless draw?   (M_ _ _)

88. My watch loses two minutes every three hours. If I put it right at eleven am today, what time would it show at eleven am the day after tomorrow?

(_ _ _ _ _ _ _am)

Each of the following rows of numbers follows a different rule. Write the missing number in the brackets.

89.   6 , 7 , 10 , 15 , (_ _ _)

90.   0 , 3.5 , 7 , 10.5 , (_ _ _)

91.   2 , 8 , 32 , 128 , (_ _ _)

92.   77 , (_ _ _) , 53 , 41 , 29

In the following questions imagine that the words were written BACKWARDS and then arranged alphabetically. Now underline the correct answers in the brackets.

93. Which of these words would come LAST?

(sable , label , table , babble , arguable)

94. Which of these words would come FIRST?

(smack , crack , stack , attack , flack)

95. Which of these words would come FOURTH?

(coast , stoats , toast , boats , feast)

In the following questions use three of the numbers on the left to complete the sums. Use three different numbers and write them in the brackets.
Here is an example.

        2 , 3 , 5 , 8   : 16 = (3 + 5 + 8)

96.   3 , 7 , 12 , 15 , 30   : 12 = (-   -   )

97.   5 , 6 , 7 , 8 , 15   : 10 = (-   +   )

98.   2 , 3 , 5 , 15 , 20   : 2 = (÷   ÷   )

99.   3 , 4 , 5 , 8 , 10   : 160 = (x   x   )

100.   5 , 6 , 8 , 15 , 20   : 12 = (+   -   )

                    Athey Educational